CW00421229

ISBN 1-85608-377-2

Designed by
THE BRIDGEWATER BOOK COMPANY LTD

Write to:
Hunt & Thorpe
Laurel House, Station Approach, New Alresford,
Hampshire, SO24 9JH, UK

Hunt & Thorpe is a name used under licence by
Paternoster Publishing, PO Box 300,
Kingstown Broadway, Carlisle, CA3 0QS, UK

The rights of Barbara Smith and Lynda Murray to be identified
as the author and illustrator of this work have been asserted by them
in accordance with the Copyright, Designs and Patents Act 1988.

A CIP catalogue record for this book
is available from the British Library.

Printed In Malaysia

Let there be
Sound

Barbara Smith
Illustrated by Lynda Murray

HUNT&
THORPE

paternoster
publishing

Loud sounds for

clapping thunder and cracking rocks

crashing waves

roaring and snoring

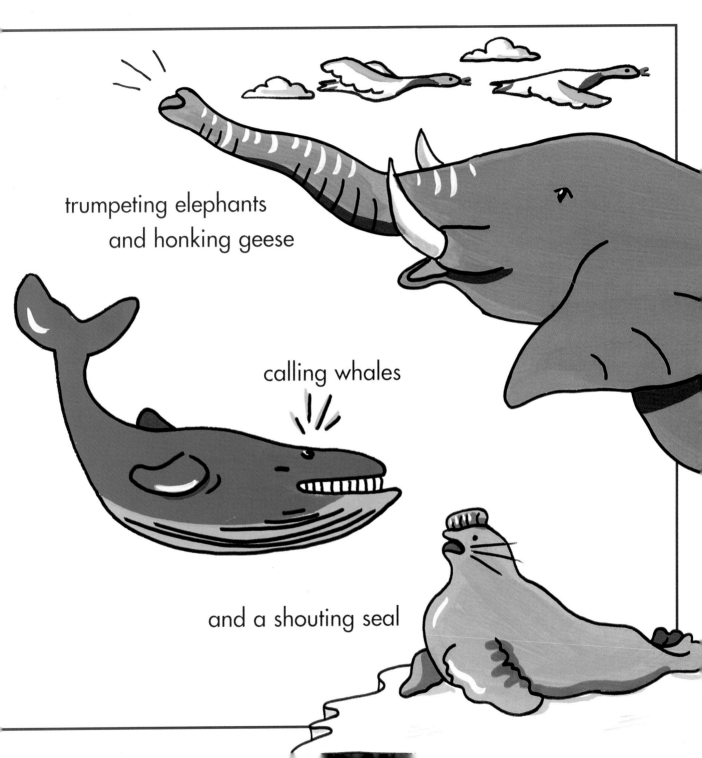

trumpeting elephants
and honking geese

calling whales

and a shouting seal

Quiet sounds for

shuffling pandas and hissing snakes

swishing tails

tapping and flapping

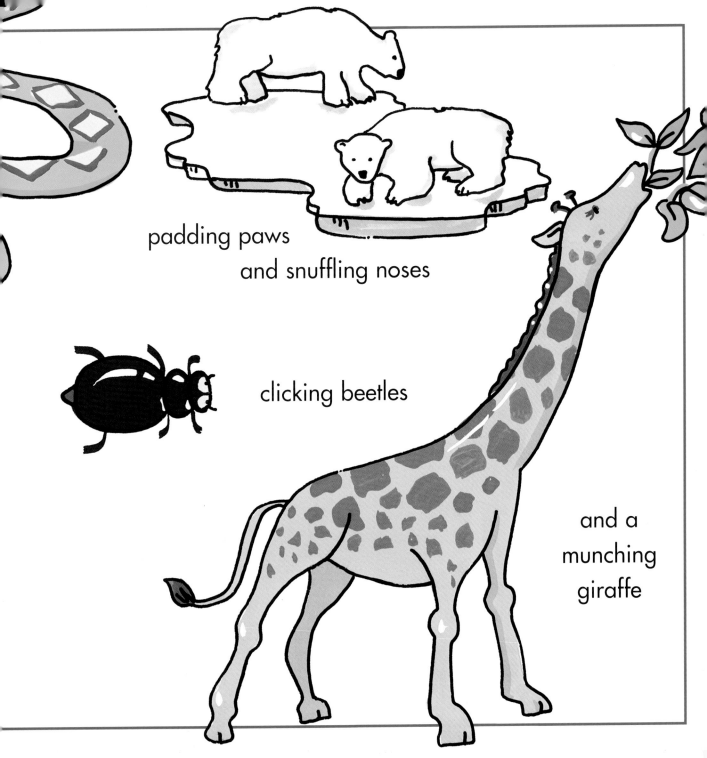

padding paws
and snuffling noses

clicking beetles

and a
munching
giraffe

Harsh sounds for

croaking frogs
and rasping crickets

squawking parrots

clashing and
smashing

cackling hens and
screeching gulls

quacking ducks

and a braying donkey

Soothing sounds for

humming birds
and buzzing bees

rustling grass

cooing and mooing

pattering raindrops
and lapping waves

gurgling streams

and a crooning chimp

High sounds for

trilling larks and fluting robins

whistling winds

squeaking and shrieking

squealing piglets and yelping jackals

scraping claws

and a piping oystercatcher

Deep sounds for

growling dogs and drumming hooves

bellowing bulls

rumbling and grumbling

booming waves
and echoing caves

thudding feet

and a chomping tortoise

Sad sounds for

mewling kittens
and howling wolves

crying seals
moaning and
groaning

whimpering puppies
and bleating lambs

whining hyenas

and a sighing swan

Happy sounds for

singing thrushes and warbling nightingales

splashing hippos

cheeping and tweeting

whinnying foals
and purring cats

chattering monkeys

and a laughing kookaburra

and the children of every nation

So we can talk and play

in the

Garden of
Creation